with best wishes—

Sushma Thaker

Vikas Stories for Children

VIOLET BOOK

A collection of interesting stories written in simple and lucid language and illustrated with beautiful multicoloured pictures.

Compiled and Edited by
C. K. Sampat
Janette Fernandes

Illustrated by
John Fernandes

Price : Rs. 19.00

NAVNEET PUBLICATIONS (I) LTD.

Bhavani Shankar Road,
Dadar, Bombay–400 028.
Phone : 430 72 86 (8 lines)

Offices : AHMADABAD, PUNE, MADRAS, NAGPUR, HYDERABAD.

N 156

CONTENTS

NAVNEET PUBLICATIONS (I) LTD.

Bombay : (1) Bhavani Shankar Road, Dadar, Bombay–400 028. (Tel. 430 72 86)
(2) **Dhanlal Bros. Distributors :** 70, Princess Street, Bombay–400 002. (Tel. 205 37 16/201 70 27)

Ahmadabad : Navneet House, Gurukul Rd., Memnagar, Ahmadabad–380 052. (Tel. 45 39 95/49 28 06)

Pune : Sita Park, 18, Shivaji Nagar, Near Bharat English School, Pune–411 005. (Tel. 32 63 64)

Nagpur : Agge Apartments, Agyaramdevi–S. T. Stand Road, Nagpur–440 018. (Tel. 72 44 11)

Madras : 30, Shriram Nagar, North Street, Alwarpet, Madras–600 018. (Tel. : 45 36 14)

Hyderabad : 6–1–142, 1st floor, Padmarao Nagar, Secunderabad–500 025. (Tel. 61 23 54)

1. The Two Pots

There was a heavy flood in a river. After three days the flood subsided. Among many other things, a copper pot and an earthen pot were floating side by side in the river.

The copper pot saw the earthen pot and said, "My friend, you are made of soft mud, and are weak. Come closer to me, if you wish. I will protect you from harm."

"Thanks for your good feelings for me," said the earthen pot. "But I dare not come closer to you. You are so strong and sturdy. I am so weak and fragile. By chance, if we crash into each other, I will shatter into a thousand tiny bits. If you are really my well-wisher, please keep away from me."

Saying so, the earthen pot smoothly floated away from the copper pot.

KEEP OVER-POWERFUL NEIGHBOURS AT A SAFE DISTANCE.

2. The Wind and the Sun

Once the Wind and the Sun had an argument.

"I am stronger than you," said the Wind.

"No, you are not," said the Sun.

Just at that moment they saw a traveller walking across the world. He was wrapped in a cloak. The Sun and the Wind agreed that whosoever of them could separate the traveller from his cloak should be declared the stronger.

The Wind took the first turn. He blew with all his might to tear the traveller's cloak from his shoulders. But the harder he blew, the tighter the traveller gripped the cloak to his body. The struggle went on till the Wind's turn was over.

Now it was the Sun's turn. The Sun smiled warmly. The traveller felt the warmth of the smiling Sun. Soon he let the cloak fall open. The Sun's smile grew warmer and warmer ...... hotter and hotter. Now the traveller no longer needed his cloak. He took it off and dropped it on the ground. The Sun was declared stronger than the Wind.

BRUTE FORCE CAN'T ACHIEVE WHAT A GENTLE SMILE CAN.

3. The Villager and Spectacles

There was a villager. He was illiterate. He did not know how to read and write. He often saw people wearing spectacles for reading books or papers. He thought, "If I have spectacles, I can also read like these people. I must go to a town and buy a pair of spectacles for me."

So one day he went to a town. He entered a spectacles shop. He asked the shopkeeper for a pair of spectacles for reading. The shopkeeper gave him various pairs of spectacles and a book. The villager tried all the spectacles one by one. But he could not read anything. He told the shopkeeper that all those spectacles were useless for him. The shopkeeper gave him a doubtful look. Then he looked at the book. It was upside down. The shopkeeper said, "Perhaps you don't know how to read."

The villager said, "No, I don't. I want to buy spectacles so that I can read like others. But I can't read with any of these spectacles."

The shopkeeper suppressed his laughter with great difficulty when he learnt the real difficulty of his illiterate customer.

He explained to the villager, "My dear friend, you are very simple and ignorant. Spectacles don't help to read and write. They merely help you to see better. First of all you must learn to read and write."

IGNORANCE IS BLINDNESS.

4. As You Sow, So Shall You Reap

One night three thieves stole a lot of money from a rich man's house. They put the money in a bag and went into a forest. They felt very hungry. There was no food in the forest. So one of them went to a nearby village to buy food. The other two remained in the forest to take care of the bag of money.

The thief that went for food had an evil idea. He ate his food at a hotel. Then he bought food for his two mates in the forest. He mixed a strong poison with the food. He thought, "Those two will eat this poisoned food and die. Then I will get all the money for myself."

Meanwhile, the two wicked men in the forest decided to kill their mate on his return. They thought that they would then divide the money between the two of them.

All the three wicked men carried out their cruel plans. The thief who wanted all the money for himself came to the forest with the poisoned food. The two men in the forest fell upon him and killed him. Then they ate the poisoned food and died.

Thus, these evil people met with an evil end.

EVIL BEGETS EVIL.

5. The Moneylender and his Purse

Once a village moneylender lost his purse. He announced a reward of a hundred rupees to the person who found it and returned it to him. A poor farmer found it. It contained one thousand rupees. The farmer was poor and needy but, at the same time, he was an honest man. He went to the moneylender and returned the purse to him.

The moneylender opened the purse and counted the money in it. It was one thousand rupees. Then he said to the farmer, "You are a smart fellow. You have taken your reward beforehand."

The farmer angrily asked, "What do you mean?"

The moneylender said, "I mean what I say. The purse contained eleven hundred rupees. But now there are one thousand rupees in it. This means that you have already taken the reward money from the purse."

The farmer said, "I have not taken any money from the purse. Let us go to the Sarpanch and settle the matter."

So they went to the Sarpanch. The Sarpanch heard both the parties. He felt sure that the moneylender was dishonest.

He asked the moneylender, "Are you sure that your purse contained eleven hundred rupees?"

The moneylender said, "Yes, Sir."

The Sarpanch said, "Then this purse is not yours."

And the Sarpanch gave away the purse to the farmer.

A WRONGDOER HAS TO PAY A HEAVY PRICE FOR HIS WRONG ACT.

6. The Farmer and his Sons

A farmer had five sons. They were strong and hardworking. But they always quarrelled with one another. Sometimes, they even fought. The farmer wanted his sons to stop quarrelling and fighting. He wanted them to live in peace. Plain words of advice or rebuke did not have much effect on these young people.

The farmer always thought what to do to keep his children united. One day he found an answer to his problem. So he called all his sons together. He showed them a bundle of sticks and said, "I want any of you to break these sticks without separating them from the bundle."

Each of the five sons tried one by one. They used their full strength and skill. But none of them could break the sticks.

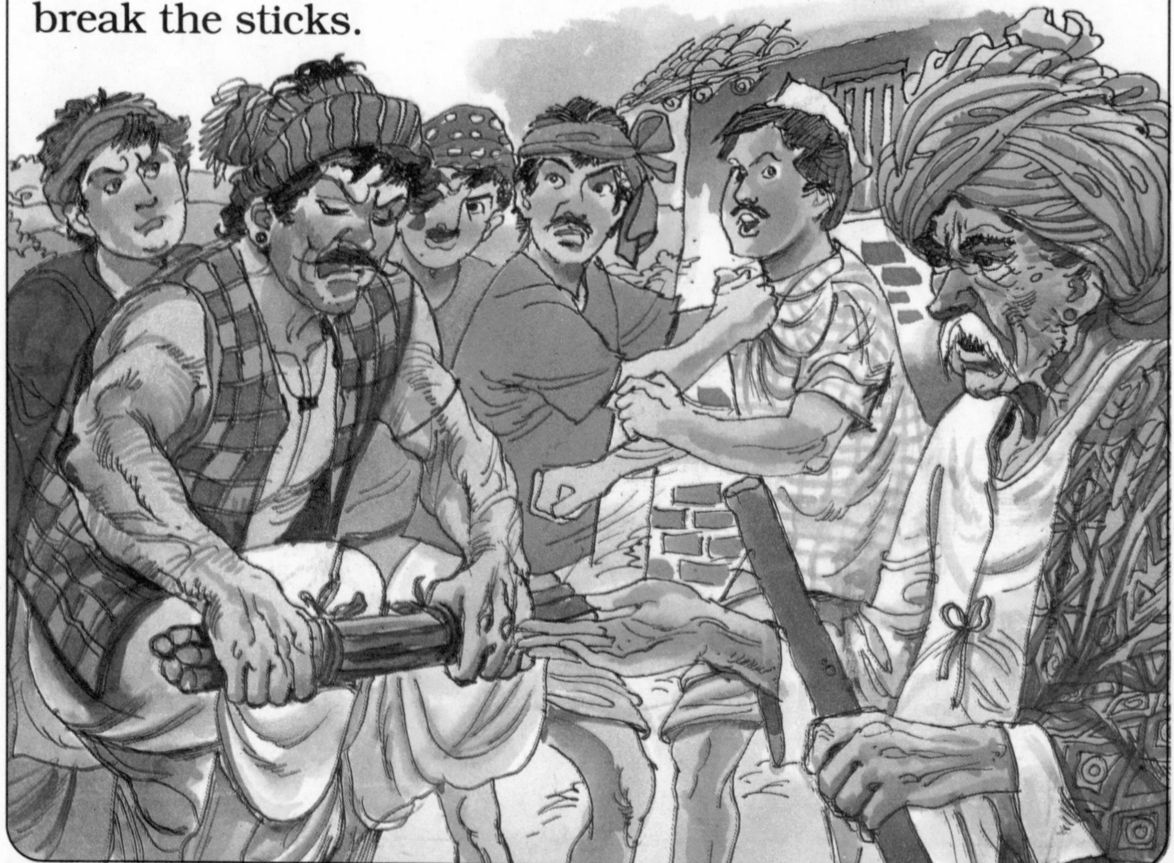

Then the old man separated the sticks and gave each of them just a single stick to break. They could break the sticks easily.

The farmer said, "A single stick by itself is weak. It is strong as long as it is tied up in a bundle. Likewise, you will be strong if you are united. You will be weak if you are divided."

UNITED WE STAND, DIVIDED WE FALL.

7. The Jovial Knight

Long, long ago, there lived a brave knight. He had shown rare bravery in many battles. He was an ace sword fighter and a champion rider. He was nobleminded, too. He always helped the poor and the needy. He protected the weak. Naturally, people loved him, admired him and respected him.

The knight, however, had a secret which was not known to most of the people, not even to his close friends. He was quite bald. He wore a wig to cover his bald head. The wig was so perfect and fitted his head so well that no one could make out that he was bald.

One day the knight and some of his friends went hunting. As they were riding along on their horses, a strong gust of wind blew off the knight's hat along with his wig.

Sudden discovery of the knight's baldness amused his friends. They never knew that their jovial friend was bald. They laughed at him and said, "Why, you are as bald as an egg. You always posed yourself as a young man and fooled us."

"Yes, I always tried to hide my baldness. But, at the same time, I was sure that my secret would be out some day. After all, when my own hair did not stay with me, how could I expect someone else's hair to stay with me forever?" said the knight and laughed heartily.

When the friends saw the knight laughing at himself, they felt sorry for laughing at him. They said, "You are really a great sport."

HE WHO CAN LAUGH AT HIMSELF WILL NEVER BECOME A LAUGHING STOCK.

8. The Peshwa and the Farmer

Bajirao Peshwa was a great commander of the Maratha Army. Once he was returning to his capital after fighting many successful battles. On the way he camped with his army in Malva. His soldiers were very tired and hungry after a long march. They did not have enough food to eat.

Bajirao called one of his captains and commanded, "Go with a hundred armed soldiers to the countryside. Cut corn from the fields and bring it to the camp for our army."

So the captain went to the countryside with a hundred armed soldiers. On the way they met a farmer. The captain said to the farmer, "Please take us to the biggest cornfield in this area." So the farmer took them to a very big cornfield. The captain ordered the soldiers to cut the corn and put it into their bags. The farmer requested the captain, "Sir, please don't cut any corn from this field. I will take you to another field where the crop is ripe and ready."

So the captain and the soldiers went with the farmer to another cornfield which was a few miles away from there. It was a small field. The farmer said, "Sir, please cut from this field as much corn as you need."

The captain angrily asked the farmer, "Why did you make us ride a long distance for this small field? This field is much smaller than the former one."

The farmer politely said, "Sir, please don't be angry. That field was not mine. This one is mine and so I have brought you here."

The farmer's reply cooled down the captain's anger. He rode back to the Peshwa without any corn and narrated his experience to him. The Peshwa then realised his own mistake. He went himself to the farmer's cornfield. He paid the farmer the price of corn in gold and collected all the corn from the field.

9. The Four Friends

Four friends lived in a village. Three of them were very learned, but they were absolutely without common sense. The fourth one was not much learned, but he possessed sound common sense.

One day, the four friends set out for the capital of the King to make their fortune. There was a jungle on their way. As they were passing through the jungle, they saw a heap of bones under a tree.

One of the learned friends observed the bones and said, "These are the bones of a lion. With the help of my learning, I can put these bones together and make a skeleton of the dead animal."

Another learned man said, "With the help of my learning, I can stuff the skeleton with flesh and blood and cover it with the skin."

The third learned man said, "With the power of my learning, I can put life into the lifeless body of the animal."

The wise man who possessed sound common sense warned his learned friends against the danger of bringing the lion back to life.

One of the learned men said, "This idiot is jealous of our learning. Let us not listen to him." The other two agreed with him. So the wise man ran off as fast as his legs could carry him.

The three learned men got busy to make use of their learning.

The first one put the bones together and made a skeleton.

The second one stuffed the skeleton with flesh and blood and covered it with the skin.

The third one put life into the lifeless body of the lion.

As soon as the lion came back to life, he roared loudly and killed the three learned men.

The fourth friend's common sense helped him to save himself.

WRONG USE OF LEARNING CAN BE DISASTROUS.

10. Birbal, the Wise

One day, a rich merchant came to Birbal, the Wise. He said to Birbal, "I have seven servants in my house. One of them has stolen my bag of precious pearls. Please find out the thief."

So Birbal went to the rich man's house. He called all the seven servants in a room. He gave a stick to each one of them. Then he said, "These are magic sticks. Just now all these sticks are equal in length. Keep them with you and return them to me tomorrow. If there is a thief in the house, his stick will grow an inch longer by tomorrow."

The servant who had stolen the bag of pearls was frightened. He thought, "If I cut a piece of one inch from my stick, I won't be caught." So he cut the stick and made it short by an inch.

The next day Birbal collected the sticks from the servants. He found that one servant's stick was short by an inch. Birbal pointed his finger at him and said, "Here is the thief." The servant confessed his crime. He returned the bag of pearls. He was sent to jail.

11. The Emperor and the Old Man

A Japanese Emperor had a set of twenty flowerpots. It was the finest collection of its kind in the world. The Emperor was very proud of his rare collection.

One day, one of the officers of the Emperor broke a flowerpot by accident. The Emperor was very angry. He passed death sentence on the officer. But before the man was put to death, an old man came to know about it. He went to the Emperor's court and said, "I know the art of repairing a broken flowerpot. Once I have repaired it, it will look its original self."

The Emperor felt very happy to hear the claim of the old man. He showed the old man the collection of his flowerpots. He said, "Here are nineteen flowerpots. One flowerpot from the set of twenty is broken. Repair the broken flowerpot and I'll pay you whatever you ask for." The old man raised his stick and broke all the nineteen flowerpots.

The Emperor was red with anger. He cried out, "You idiot! What have you done?" The old man coolly replied, "I have done my duty. Each of these flowerpots would have taken one human life. Now you can take only one life, and that is mine."

The old man's wisdom and boldness pleased the Emperor. He forgave the old man and the officer, too.

12. The Song of Four Fools

In a tall tree in a jungle lived a little black bird. Every morning it sang sweetly. Down on the ground fell a few grains of gold from its beak as it sang. One morning a fowler saw the grains of gold dropping down from its beak. He said to himself, "What a luck! I must catch this bird and carry it home. Everyday it will give me grains of gold. Soon I will be a very rich man."

The fowler, then, spread a net on the ground and sprinkled some grains of rice there. The black bird saw the grains of rice and flew into the net. The fowler caught the bird and carried it home.

From that day on, the fowler got a few grains of gold every day and soon he became a very rich man. Then he thought that he must get some fame and honour. So he made a beautiful cage of gold and put the bird into it. Then he gave away the cage of gold and the bird to the King and said, "Your Majesty, this bird will sing sweet songs in your palace and give you grains of gold every day." The King was glad to receive the present. He gave the fowler a seat of honour in his court.

Soon, the King also had a lot of gold. He gave away the cage of gold and the bird to his beloved queen. The queen set the bird free and gave the cage of gold to the royal goldsmith. She said to the goldsmith, "Make for me the most beautiful ornaments from this cage of gold."

The bird flew away back into the jungle. Every morning it sang "The song of four fools". It sang, "I flew into the fowler's net. I was the first fool. The fowler gave me away to the King. The fowler was the second fool. The King gave me away to the queen. The King was the third fool. The queen set me free. The queen was the fourth fool."

13. The Fruitseller and the Grocer

One day a grocer borrowed a balance and weights from a fruitseller. After a few days the fruitseller asked the grocer to return his balance and weights to him.

The grocer said, "Mice ate away your balance and weights. I am sorry that I can't return them to you."

The false excuse of the dishonest grocer made the fruitseller very angry. But he controlled his temper and said, "Never mind. I can't blame you. It is my bad luck."

Then one day the fruitseller said to the grocer, "I am going to a town to do some shopping. Please send your son with me. We will come back tomorrow."

So the grocer sent his son with the fruitseller. The next day the fruitseller returned alone from the town.

"Where is my son?" asked the grocer.

"A stork carried away your son," replied the fruitseller.

"You liar! How can a stork carry away such a big boy?" shouted the grocer angrily.

"Just the same way as mice can eat away the balance and weights," said the fruitseller.

The grocer understood the point. He returned the balance and weights to the fruitseller and requested him with tearful eyes, "I did a great wrong to you. Please forgive me for my fault and return my son to me."

The fruitseller then sent the son back to his father.

SOME PEOPLE DON'T LEARN A LESSON UNLESS THEY ARE KICKED HARD.

14. The Idiot and the Rogues

Once upon a time there lived in a village an idiot whom even a village child could cheat easily. No matter how hard he tried to be clever, someone or the other made a fool of him.

One day the idiot was going to the weekly market to sell his horse and goat. He hung a bell from the collar round the goat's neck. He tied one end of a rope to the horse's tail and another to the goat's collar. He then mounted the horse and rode for the marketplace.

Some rogues, who knew the idiot, followed him. On the way one of the rogues tied the bell to the tail of the horse and ran away with the goat. The bell tied to the tail went on ringing and the idiot believed that the goat was following him.

Some time later, another rogue stopped the idiot on the way and said, "Please excuse me, Sir. Will you kindly tell me why you have tied a bell to your horse's tail?" The idiot looked behind. He was surprised and shocked to find the goat missing.

In the meantime, a third rogue came there and said to the idiot, "Sir, I saw a man running away with your goat. If you wish, I will chase the thief on your horse and get back your stolen goat."

The idiot at once got down from the horse and gave it to that rogue. The rogue bade him goodbye and drove away the horse.

The poor idiot waited for a long time in the hope of getting back his animals. But he saw no sign of their coming and at last returned home empty-handed.

Far away somewhere, the rogues were singing :

Jingle bell, jingle bell, jingle all the way,
Keep on singing day and night, life is but a play.

A FOOL AND HIS FORTUNE
DON'T STAY TOGETHER FOR A LONG TIME.

Published & Printed by : Navneet Publications (India) Ltd. 95 (4)